My Dd Boo

Name _____

Hey diddle diddle,
The cat and the fiddle,
The cow jumped over the moon.

Harcourt Brace School Publishers

Read "Hey Diddle Diddle" with children. Invite them to pantomime appropriate actions while reciting. Then have children circle each *D* and *d* in the rhyme and in the art.

Phonics Activity Book

IDENTIFYING
Dd

3

DD   dd

☐ inosaur

☐ ish

4 **PRINTING** *Dd*

Discuss the page with children. Have children find *Dd* and then trace and write the letters. Children can complete each word with *D* or *d* and draw dinner on the dinosaur's plate.

Phonics Activity Book

Mm Is for Mouse

Name _____

To Market

To market, to market,
To buy a plum bun;

Market

Mouse House

Read "To Market" with children. Have children identify the letter *Mm*. Then have them match and circle each *M* and *m* in the poem and in the art.

IDENTIFYING
Mm

7

Name _____

MM   mm

Mouse ▢**arket**

 ▢**uffins**

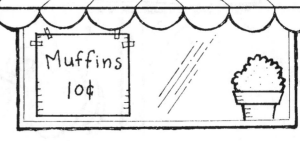

Muffins 10¢

 ▢**ops**

 ▢**ilk**

8

PRINTING
Mm

Discuss the page with children. Have children find *Mm* and then trace and write the letters. Children can complete the words on the sign with *M* or *m*.

Phonics Activity Book

TREASURY OF LITERATURE

PHONICS ACTIVITY BOOK

KINDERGARTEN

HARCOURT BRACE & COMPANY

Orlando   Atlanta   Austin   Boston   San Francisco   Chicago   Dallas   New York
Toronto   London

CONTENTS

Handwriting models in this program have been used with permission of the publisher, Zaner-Bloser, Inc., Columbus, OH.

Printed in the United States of America

ISBN 0-15-305358-5

Pp Is for Peanut

Name _____

Pumpkin Patch

A Peanut

A peanut sat on the railroad track,
Its heart was all a-flutter—
Choo-choo train comes round the bend,
Toot! Toot! Peanut butter!

Anonymous

P P

p p

Picnic Place

☐ ine   ☐ ark

☐ ie   ☐ ears

PRINTING
Pp

Discuss the page with children. Have them find *Pp* and then trace and write the letters. Children can complete each word on the park sign and in the picnic scene with *P* or *p*.

Phonics Activity Book

My Ss Book

Name _____

Sally go round the sun,
Sally go round the moon,
Sally go round the chimney pots
On a Saturday afternoon.

Read "Sally go round the sun" with children. Invite them to join hands and sway at their tables while reciting the rhyme. Then have them circle each S and 's in the rhyme and in the art.

IDENTIFYING
Ss

15

S s

s s

☐ ocks

☐ oap

☐ eeds

SUPER STORE

SALE

SOCKS
SHOES
SNEAKERS
& STUFF

SALLY'S
SACK

SOAP

SUNFLOWER
SQUASH
SEEDS
SEEDS

16 PRINTING *Ss*

Discuss the page with children. Have them find *Ss* and then trace and write the letters. Then have children name the items Sally bought at the store and finish each word with *S* or *s*.

Phonics Activity Book

Ss  sandwich

Phonics Activity Book

Help children identify each picture along the path. Have them color the items whose names begin with the same sound as *sandwich*. Then have children count the number of pictures that have been colored.

LISTENING FOR
/s/s

17

 S s

   □ eal

  7 □ even

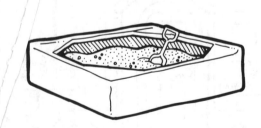   □ andbox

18 **RELATING LETTERS AND SOUNDS** /s/s

Have children circle the picture in each row whose name begins with /s/s. Then have them complete the corresponding words by printing S or s in each box.

Phonics Activity Book

Ff Is for Fish

Name _____

The Fish

I hold my fingers like a fish,
And wave them as I go.
See them swimming with a swish,
So swiftly to and fro.

Phonics Activity Book

Read "The Fish" with children, making waving motions with your hands. Then have them circle each *F* and *f* in the rhyme. Then have children count the number of fish in the water.

IDENTIFYING
Ff
19

F F f f

5 ☐ ive

☐ ish

Fish Food

☐ ood

Pet Fish
for Sale

Discuss the page with children. Have them find *Ff* and then trace and write the
letters. Children can complete each word with *F* or *f* and then draw five fish in
the bowl.

Phonics Activity Book

Bb Is for Bear

Name _____

Teddy Bear

Teddy bear, teddy bear, turn around.

Teddy bear, teddy bear, touch the ground.

Teddy bear, teddy bear, read the news.

Teddy bear, teddy bear, brush your shoes.

Read "Teddy Bear" with children. While reciting the rhyme, invite children to pantomime the actions. Then have them circle each *B* and *b* in the rhyme and in the art.

Phonics Activity Book

IDENTIFYING
Bb

23

Name _____

B B   b b

☐erry   ☐ush

☐ear

☐ird   ☐ee

24   PRINTING *Bb*

Discuss the page with children. Have them find *Bb* and then trace and write the letters. Children can complete the words by printing *B* or *b* in each box.

Phonics Activity Book

Tt Is for Turtle

Name _____

A Big Turtle

A big turtle sat
on the end of a log,
Watching a tadpole
turn into a frog.

Unknown

Phonics Activity Book

Read "A Big Turtle" with children. Then have children circle each *T* and *t* in the rhyme and finish the art by drawing a picture of a big turtle sitting on the log.

IDENTIFYING
Tt

27

Name _____

T T t t

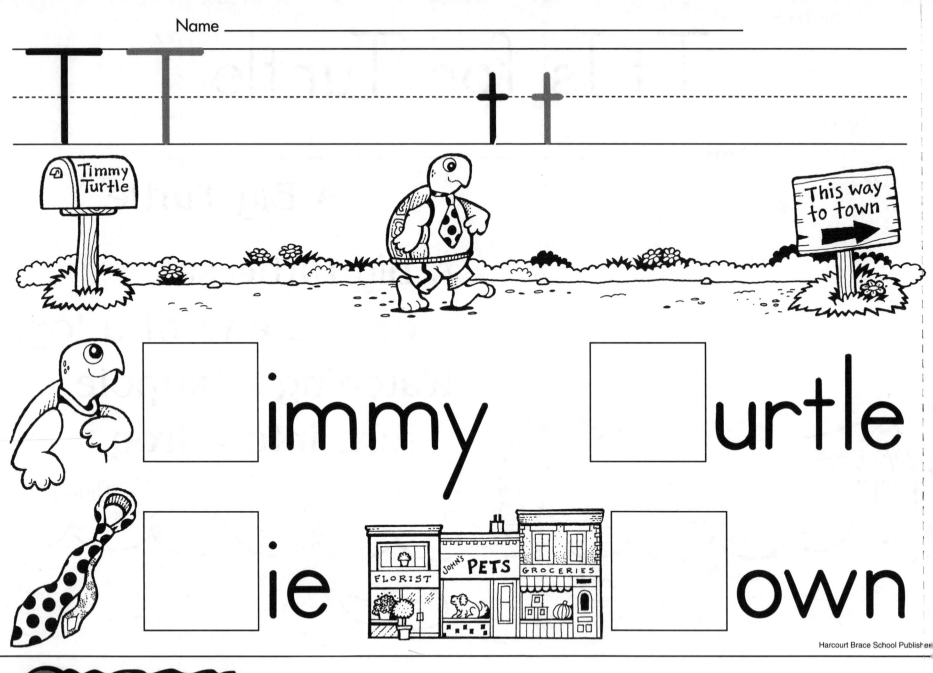

☐immy ☐urtle

☐ie ☐own

Discuss the page with children. Have them find *Tt* and then trace and write the letters. Have them identify each picture and then complete the words by printing *T* or *t* in each box.

Phonics Activity Book

T t

turtle

Phonics Activity Book

Help children identify each picture. Have them color the items whose names begin with the same sound as *turtle*. After the pictures have been colored, have children use a finger to trace the path the turtle will take to town.

LISTENING FOR **29**
/t/t

 **T t**

Name _____

   □urkey

  □iger

  □ent

 **RELATING LETTERS AND SOUNDS** /t/t

Have children circle the picture in each row whose name begins with /t/t. Then have them complete the corresponding words by printing T or t in each box.

Phonics Activity Book

Harcourt Brace School Publishers

Ll Is for Lamb

Name _____

Two Little Lambs

This little lamb wants grass.
This little lamb wants hay.
Give them all that they can eat,
And let them munch away.

Laurel Lane

Phonics Activity Book

Read "Two Little Lambs" with children. Then have them circle each *L* and *l* in the rhyme and in the art.

IDENTIFYING
Ll

31

Name _____

L l

_adybug

_og

_eaf

_izard

PRINTING
Ll

Discuss the scene with children. Have children find *Ll* and then trace and write
the letters. Have children complete each word by printing *L* or *l* in the box.

Phonics Activity Book

Apple Tree

Away up high in the
apple tree,
Two red apples smiled
at me.
I shook the tree
as hard as I could,
And down came
the apples.
Mmmmmm,
were they good!

FOLD

My Aa Book

Name _____

Harcourt Brace School Publishers

Phonics Activity Book

Read "Apple Tree" with children. Then have them circle each A and a in the poem. Have children cut out the page and fold it along the fold line to make a book about Aa. Children can finish the page by drawing apples in the tree.

IDENTIFYING
Aa

35

Name _____

A A   a a

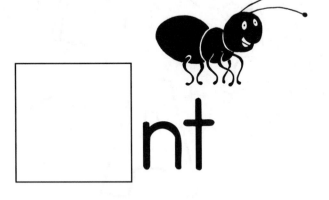

☐ nt

☐ lligator

☐ corn

☐ nteater

36 **PRINTING** *Aa*

Have children find Aa and then trace and write the letters. Help children identify each picture. Then have them complete the words by printing *A* or *a* in each box.

Phonics Activity Book

Cc Is for Cat

Name _____

**Great A, little a,
Bouncing B,
The cat is in the cupboard and
Can't see me!**

Cake Mix

Cat Food

Cat Food

Cocoa

Phonics Activity Book

Read the rhyme with children. Then have them circle each C and c in the rhyme and in the art. To finish the scene, children can draw themselves hiding from the cat.

IDENTIFYING
Cc

37

C C

c c

Corn

Carrots

 ☐ arrots  ☐ orn

 ☐ at  ☐ ow

38 PRINTING *Cc*

Discuss the scene with children. Have them find *Cc* and then trace and write the letters. Have children complete each word by printing *C* or *c*.

Phonics Activity Book

Harcourt Brace School Publishers

My Zz Book

Name _____

BUZZ

BUZZ

BUZZ

ZEKE

THE ZOO

ZEBRA

BEAR

**A fuzzy old bear
at the zoo
Could always find
something to do.**

Phonics Activity Book

Read the poem with children. Have them tell what they think the bear might do.
Then have children circle each Z and z in the poem and in the art.

IDENTIFYING
Zz

41

Name _____

Zz   Zz

☐ebra

☐igzag

☐ipper

Have children find *Zz* and then trace and write the letters. Help children identify each picture. Then have them complete the words by printing *Z* or *z* in each box and trace each letter *z* to finish the art.

Phonics Activity Book

Rr Is for Rain

Name _____

Rain

Rain on the green grass
And rain on the tree,
Rain on the rooftop,
But not on me.

Anonymous

Phonics Activity Book

Read "Rain" with children. Then have them circle each *R* and *r* in the poem. To finish the art, have children draw themselves in the picture.

Name _____

R R   r r

□ ainbow

□ accoon

□ abbit

□ ose

46 PRINTING *Rr*

Have children find *Rr* and then trace and write the letters. Help children identify each picture. Then have them complete each word by printing *R* or *r* in the box.

Phonics Activity Book

Kk Is for Kite

Name _____

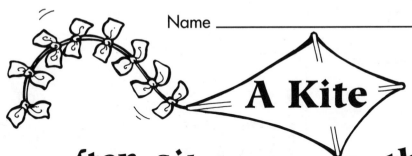

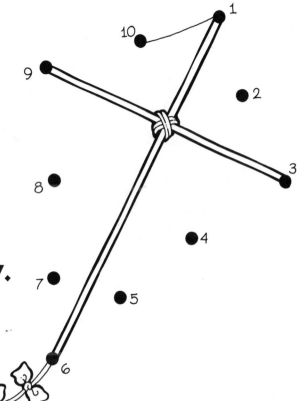

A Kite

I often sit and wish that I
Could be a kite up in the sky,
And ride upon a breeze and go
Whichever way I chanced to blow.

Anonymous

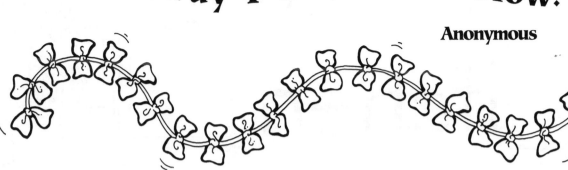

Phonics Activity Book

Read "A Kite" with children. Then have them circle each *K* and *k* in the poem.
Have children connect the dots to form a kite.

IDENTIFYING
Kk

49

K K   k k

[ ]ing

[ ]eys

[ ]itchen

PRINTING
Kk

Discuss the page with children. Have children find *Kk* and then trace and write the letters. Children can complete each word with *K* or *k*.

Phonics Activity Book

My Uu Book

Name _____

Umbrella

Here is my umbrella.
It will keep me dry.
When I go walking
in the rain
I hold it up so high.

FOLD

Read "Umbrella" with children. Have them circle each *U* and *u* in the rhyme. Have children cut out the page and fold it to make a book. Then children can draw themselves standing under the umbrella.

IDENTIFYING
Uu

53

Name _____

U U U   u u

☐ p

☐ nder

☐ mbrella

54

PRINTING
Uu

Have children find *Uu* and then trace and write the letters. Have children identify each picture and then complete each word by printing *U* or *u* in the box.

Phonics Activity Book

My Jj Book

Name _____

Jack-in-the-Box

Jack-in-the-box
Sits so still.
Won't you jump out?
"Yes, I will!"

Phonics Activity Book

Read "Jack-in-the-Box" with children. Have children circle each *J* and *j* in the poem and in the art. Discuss the toys shown with children and have them draw the missing Jack-in-the-box head.

IDENTIFYING
Jj

55

Name _____

J J J   j j

J j

grape jelly $1.00

toy jets $1.00

jump ropes $1.50

juice 25¢

jugs $2.50

☐ et

☐ elly

☐ ug

☐ uice

Harcourt Brace School Publishers

Discuss the page with children. Have children find *Jj* and then trace and write the letters. Children can name each picture and complete each word by printing J or *j* in the box.

Phonics Activity Book

Name _____

Inchworm

Inchworm, inchworm,
in the tree.

I see you,

but you can't see me.

FOLD

FOLD

My I Book

Phonics Activity Book

Read "Inchworm" with children. Then have them circle each *I* and *i* in the poem.
Have children fold the paper along the two fold lines to make a book about *Ii*.
Have children draw a picture of themselves in the empty space.

IDENTIFYING
Ii

59

Name _____

I I   i i

□ ron

□ ce cream

□ nsect

□ gloo

60 PRINTING
Ii

Have children find *Ii* and then trace and write the letters. Help children identify each picture and then complete the words by printing *I* or *i* in each box.

Phonics Activity Book

My O o O o Book

Name _____

The Octopus

If you should meet
an octopus

Down in the ocean blue,

Turn and swim away
real fast.

Those eight arms
might catch you!

Read "The Octopus" with children. As children repeat the rhyme, invite them to pantomime appropriate actions. Then have them circle each O and o in the rhyme. Have children cut out the page and fold it to make a book about Oo.

IDENTIFYING
Oo

63

Name _____

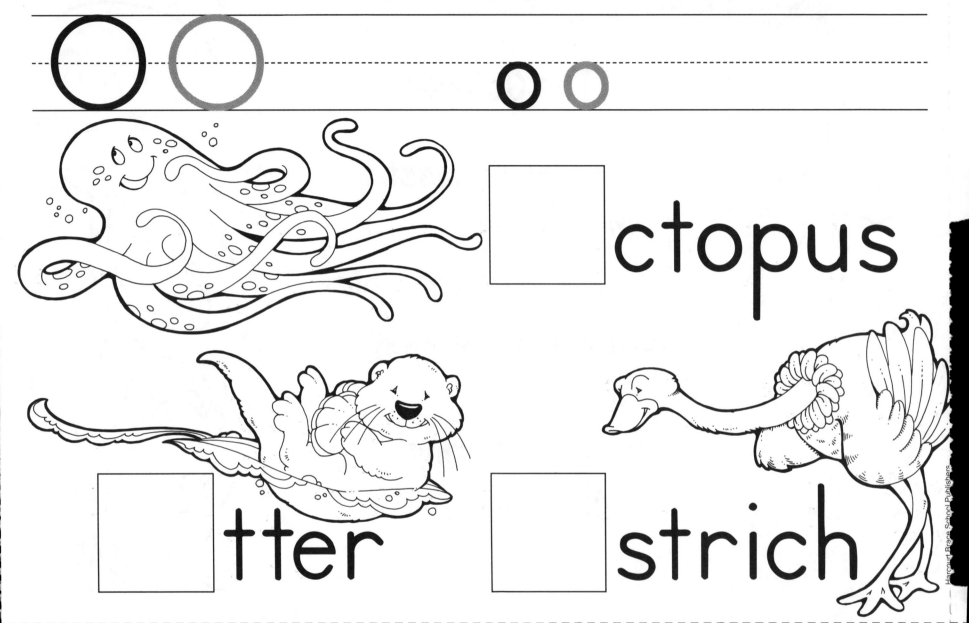

O O

o o

☐ctopus

☐tter

☐strich

Discuss the page with children. Have them find Oo and then trace and write the letters. Have children identify each picture and complete each word by printing O or o in each box.

Phonics Activity Book

Nn Is for Nest

Name _____

Robin's Nest

Houses

This is a nest for Robin.

This is a hive for Bee.

This is a hole for Bunny.

And this is a house for me.

Read "Houses" with children, demonstrating the hand motions as you read.
Then have children circle each *N* and *n* in the poem and in the art. To finish the
page, have them draw a bird in the nest.

Phonics Activity Book

IDENTIFYING
Nn
65

N N   n n

☐ewspaper   Town News 99¢

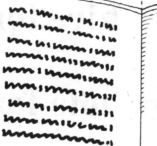

Nut Bread Recipe

☐urse   ☐ine

Discuss the page with children. Have children find *Nn* and then trace and write the letters. Children can complete each word on the newspaper with *N* or *n*.

Phonics Activity Book

Harcourt Brace School Publishers

Gg Is for Goat

Name _____

Three gray goats went walking
One lovely summer's day.
They crossed a bridge to get some grass,
But a troll got in their way.

Name _____

G G   g g

☐ arden

☐ oat

☐ oose

70   **PRINTING** *Gg*

Have children find *Gg* and then trace and write the letters. Help children identify each picture. Then have them complete each word by printing *G* or *g* in each box.

Phonics Activity Book

Hh Is for Horse

Name _____

Hobby Horse

I had a little hobby horse,
And it was dapple gray.
Its head was made of pea-straw.
Its tail was made of hay.

Phonics Activity Book

Read "Hobby Horse" with children. Have them gallop in place as they recite the rhyme. Then have children circle the letters *H* and *h* in the rhyme and in the art.

IDENTIFYING
Hh

73

Name _____

H H   h h

☐ ats for Sale

☐ orse   ☐ at

☐ ippo   ☐ at

Discuss the page with children. Have them find *Hh* and then trace and write the letters. Have children complete each word with *H* or *h* and then draw a hat on the horse and on the hippo.

Phonics Activity Book

Ee Is for Egg

Name _____

Eggs

Take a peek!
Look and see
Inside each egg.
What can it be?

Read the poem with children. Have them circle each *E* and *e* in the poem.
Discuss the kinds of baby animals that might be inside each egg. Then have
children hold up the page to a bright light to reveal what is inside each egg.

Phonics Activity Book

Name _____

EE

e e

chick

gg

turtle

gg

snake

gg

Have children find *Ee* and then trace and write the letters. Have children identify the animal inside each egg and complete the words by printing *E* or *e* in each box.

Harcourt Brace School Publishers

Phonics Activity Book

My Vv Book

Name _____

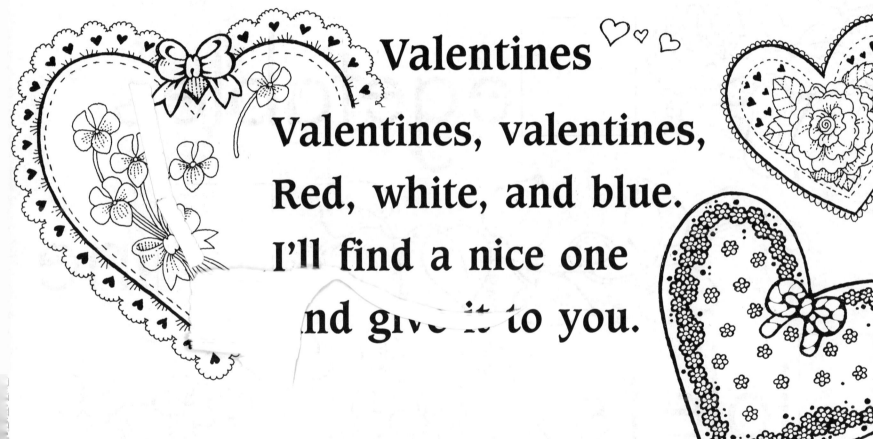

Valentines

Valentines, valentines,
Red, white, and blue.
I'll find a nice one
nd give it to you.

Read "Valentines" with children. Have them circle each *V* and *v* in the poem.
Have children decorate the page by coloring the valentines and adding hearts
of their own.

Phonics Activity Book

IDENTIFYING
Vv
79

Name _____

V V V v v

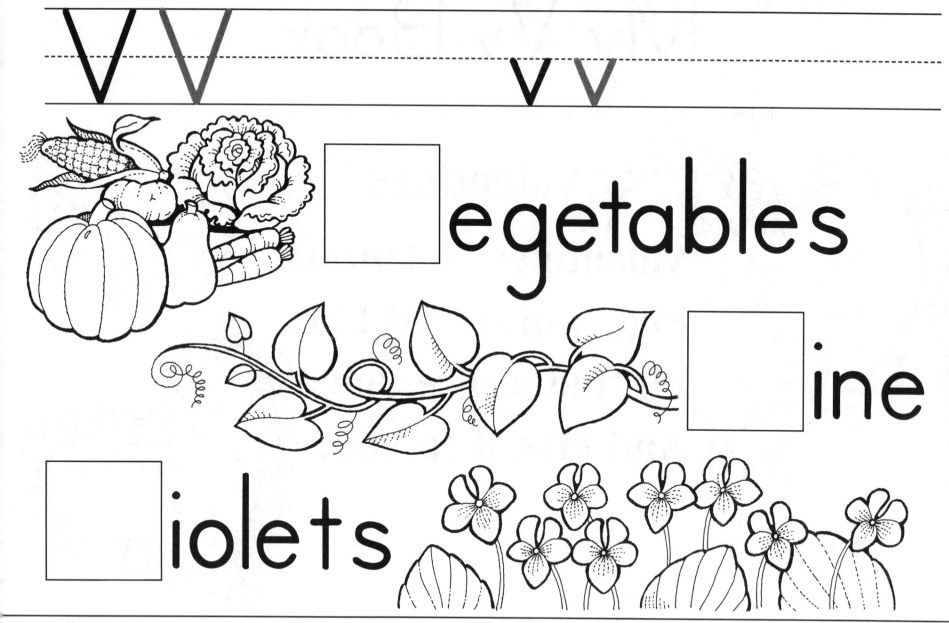

☐egetables

☐ine

☐iolets

PRINTING
Vv

Have children find *Vv* and then trace and write the letters. Discuss the pictures on the page with children and have them complete the words by printing *V* or *v* in each box.

Phonics Activity Book

My Ww Book

Name _____

Charlie Warlie had a cow,

Black and white about the brow;

Open the gate and let her through,

Charlie Warlie's old cow.

Mother Goose

Phonics Activity Book

Read the rhyme with children. Then have them find and circle each *W* and *w* in the rhyme and in the art.

IDENTIFYING
Ww

83

Name _____

W W W

w w

☐ell

☐alrus

☐ater

☐indow

PRINTING
Ww

Talk with children about the picture cluster showing the different places where water can be found. Have them find *Ww* and then trace and write the letters. Children can complete the picture names by printing *W* or *w* in each box.

Phonics Activity Book

Yy Is for Yellow

Name _____

My Flower Bed

See the blue and yellow blossoms
In the flower bed.
The daisy spreads its petals wide.
The tulip bows its head.

Your flowers

Phonics Activity Book

Read "My Flower Bed" with children. Then have them circle each Y and y in the rhyme and in the art. Have children finish the page by coloring yellow flowers on the stems.

IDENTIFYING
Yy

87

Name _____

Y Y ␣Y yy

yy

Yellow ␣ellow Things

␣o - ␣o

␣arn

␣olk

Harcourt Brace School Publi

88 PRINTING
yy

Discuss with children some things that can be yellow. Have children find *Yy* and
then trace and write the letters. Have them complete the names of yellow things
with *Y* or *y* and color the objects yellow.

Phonics Activity Book

Name _____

Queen Caroline

Queen, Queen Caroline

Washed her hair in turpentine,

Turpentine to make it shine,

Queen, Queen Caroline.

Phonics Activity Book

Read "Queen Caroline" with children. Then have them circle each Q and q in the rhyme and in the art. Have children cut out the page and fold it to make a book about Qq.

Q Q

q q

☐uilt

☐uarter

☐uail

☐uills

92 **PRINTING** *Qq*

Have children find Qq and then trace and write the letters. Help them identify each picture. Then have them trace the hidden Q or q and complete each word by printing Q or q in the box.

Phonics Activity Book

Name _____

✂

Phonics Activity Book

Have children write their name on the cover. Help them assemble the alphabet book by stapling the pages together.

Alphabet Book

93

Alphabet
Book

Phonics Activity Book

Phonics Activity Book

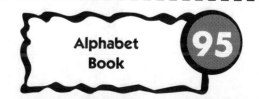